Edition Schott

Nikolai Kapustin

Николай Капустин

1937 – 2020

The End of the Rainbow

(2003)

for Piano
für Klavier
для фортепиано

opus 112

Authorized Version

ED 23034
ISMN 979-0-001-20500-9

www.schott-music.com

Mainz · London · Madrid · Paris · New York · Tokyo · Beijing
© 2021 Schott Music GmbH & Co. KG, Mainz · Printed in Germany

The End of the Rainbow

opus 112

Nikolai Kapustin
1937–2020

Allegretto (♩ = 108)

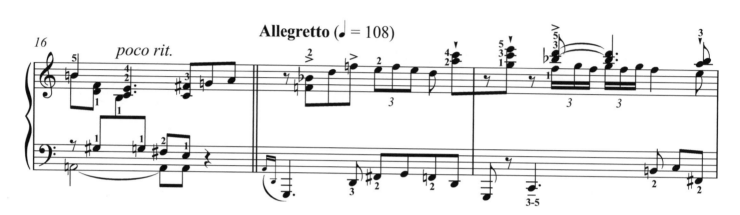

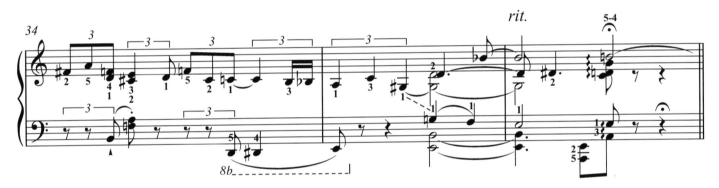

Allegretto

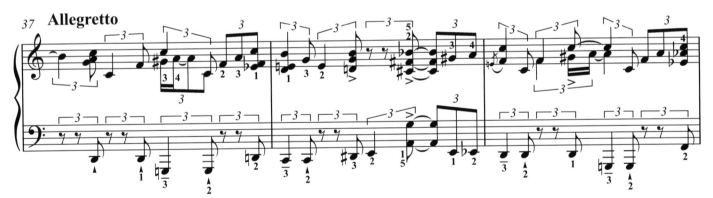

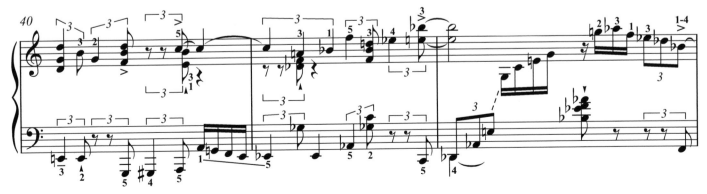

*) Ossia:

6

a tempo

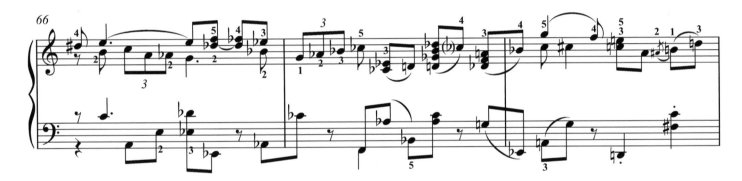

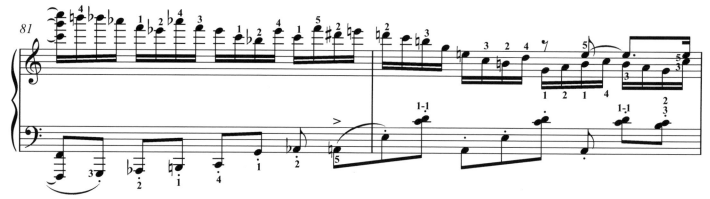

*) Ossia: etc.

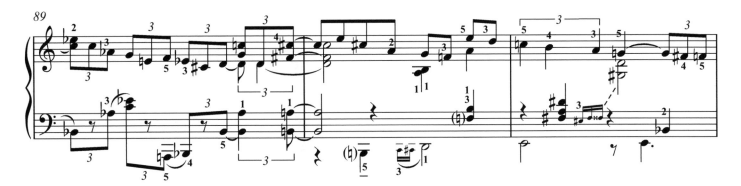

a tempo

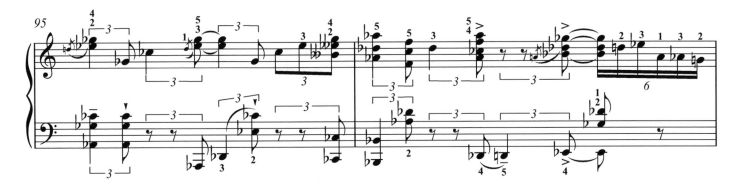

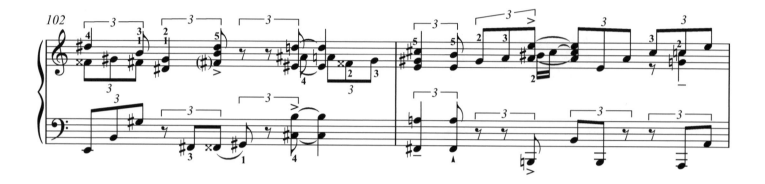

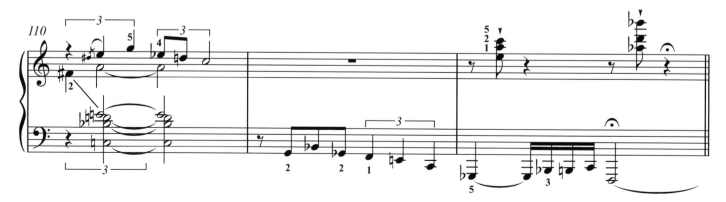

Schott Music, Mainz 59 372